JUST POP

Progressive piano solos

ARRANGED BY STEPHEN DURO

Chester Music
(A division of Music Sales Limited)
8/9 Frith Street
London W1V 5TZ

PREFACE

Here are 14 songs carefully chosen from the repertory of pop
'standards'. The songs are arranged according to difficulty,
with the easier pieces (approximately Grade II to III standard
of the Associated Board) appearing first, and the harder ones
(Grade V/VI standard) towards the end. Fingering, where
indicated, is intended as a guide only and should be altered
to suit the needs of individual players.

Stephen Duro

Visit the Music Sales Internet Music Shop
at http://www.musicsales.co.uk

This book © Copyright 1997 Chester Music
Order No. CH61280 ISBN 0-7119-6438-6

Music processed by Allegro Reproductions.
Cover design by 4i Limited.
Printed in the United Kingdom by Caligraving Limited, Thetford, Norfolk.

CONTENTS

UNCHAINED MELODY

Music by Alex North
Words by Hy Zaret

This song is characterised by a long flowing melody. Try to keep the music moving by giving a slight accent to the first beat of the tune in alternate bars.

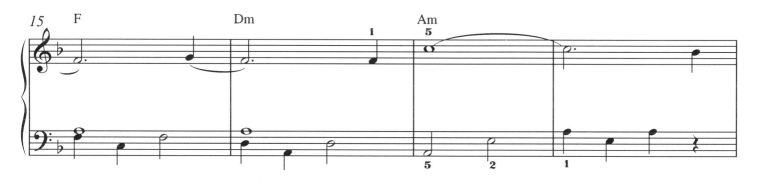

To Coda

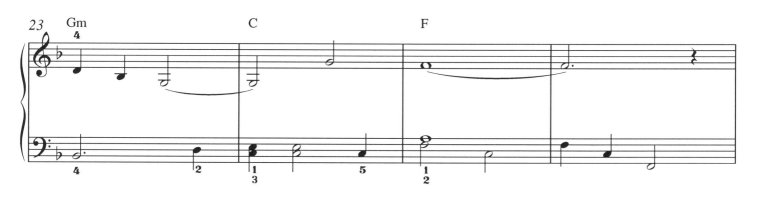

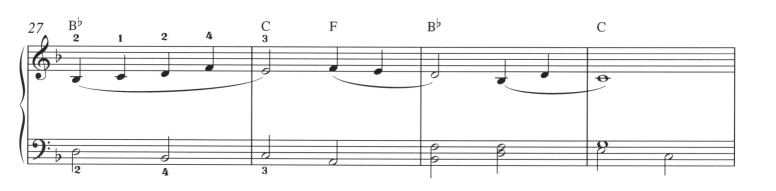

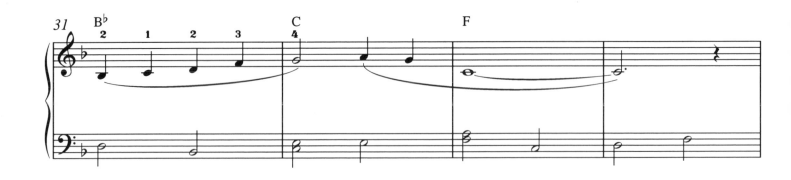

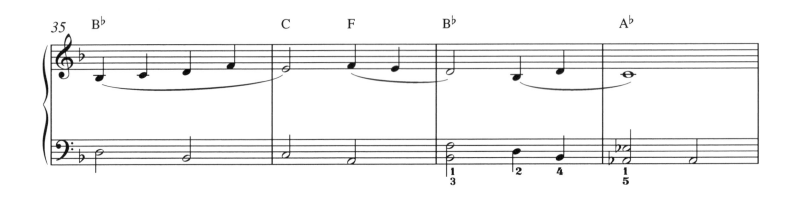

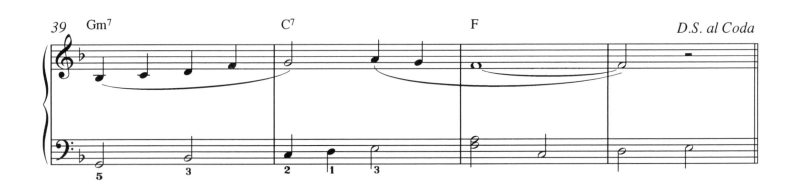

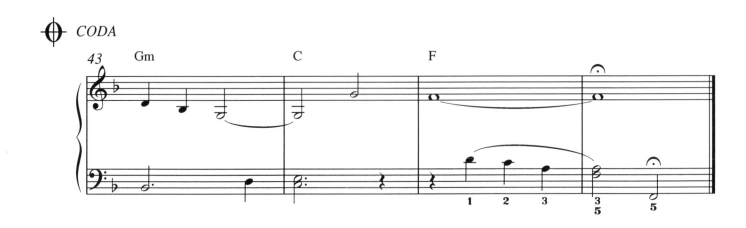

THE POWER OF LOVE

Words and music by C. deRouge, G. Mende,
J. Rush and S. Applegate

The main thing to achieve, in a ballad of this kind,
is a sense of forward motion. Keep a steady beat
and allow the music to unfold.

LOVE HURTS

Words and music by Boudleaux Bryant

A relaxed, simple interpretation suits this ballad. Try not to hurry the quaver notes which occur frequently in the melody.

CRAZY

Words and music by Willie Nelson

This song benefits from a restrained performance. The melody should be played freely, but not too slowly, with a definite 4 beats-to-the-bar feel.

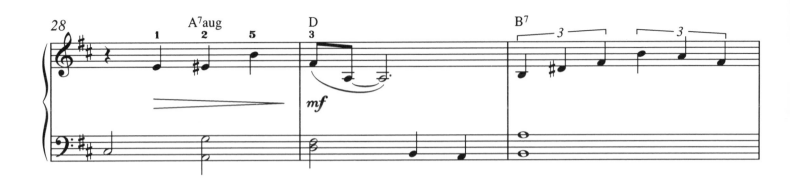

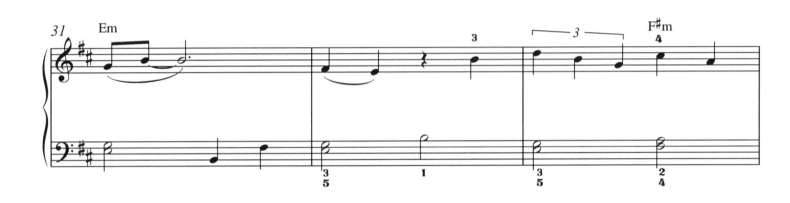

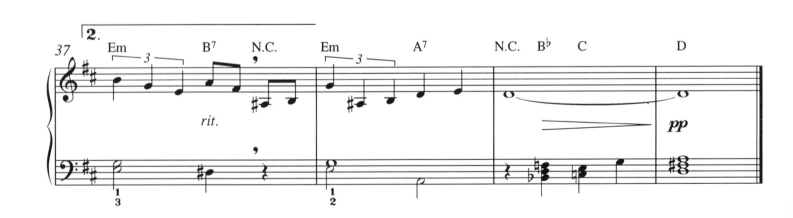

TEARS IN HEAVEN

Words and music by Eric Clapton and Will Jennings

A gentle treatment suits this song (as befits the title). You will find that spreading the left hand chords, (in bar 7, for example) adds warmth.

15

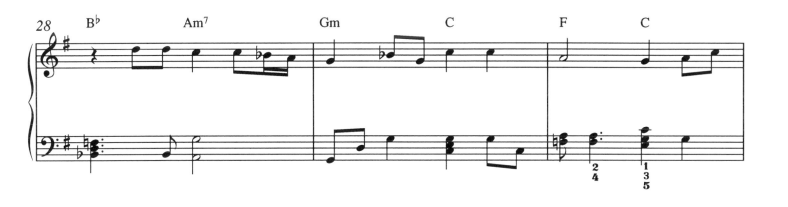

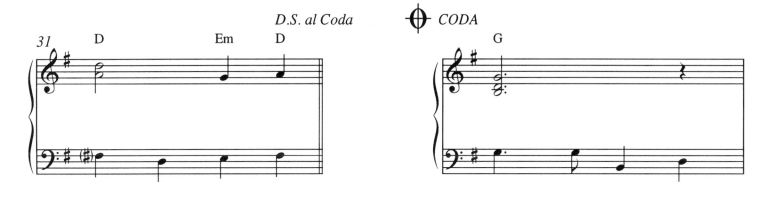

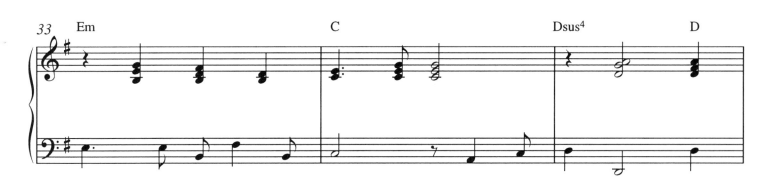

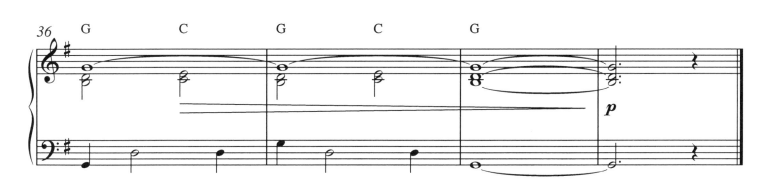

HE AIN'T HEAVY...HE'S MY BROTHER

Words by Bob Russell
Music by Bobby Scott

This song is characterised as much by fine words as it is by a good melody. There is a climactic point beginning at bar 23 so try to reflect this in your playing.

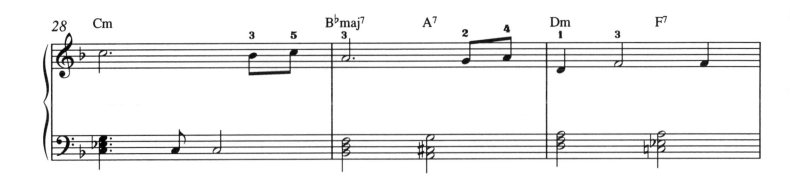

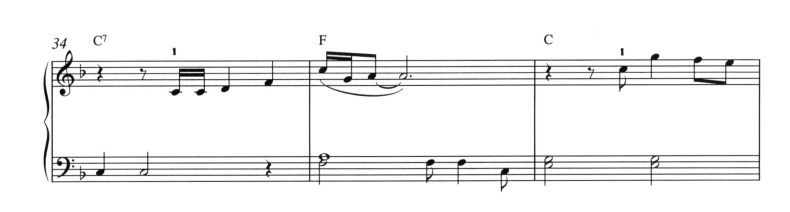

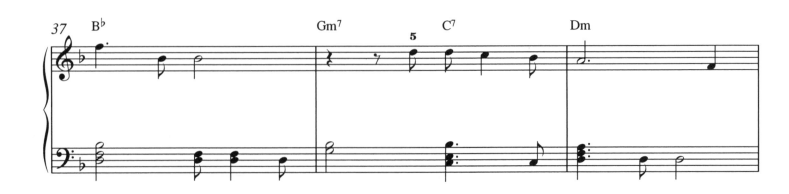

20

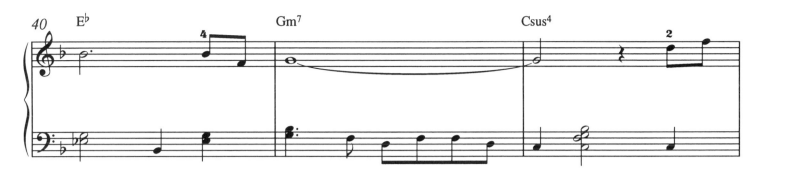

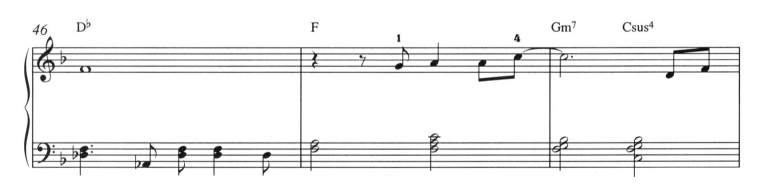

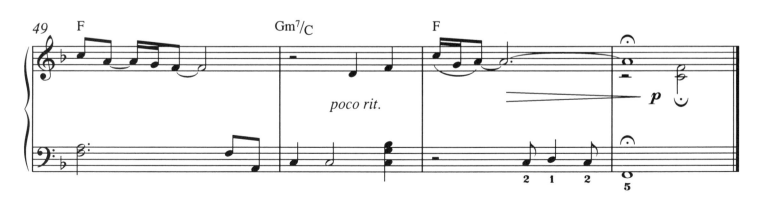

INTO THE GROOVE

Words and music by Madonna Ciccone and Steve Bray

As the title suggests, this piece needs to be played with a driving beat. The melody should also be played in a rhythmic, percussive style.

HEY JUDE

Words and music by John Lennon and Paul McCartney

This song begins simply but builds to a powerful climax. This needs to be reflected in your performance: the first 16 bars, in particular, should be played gently.

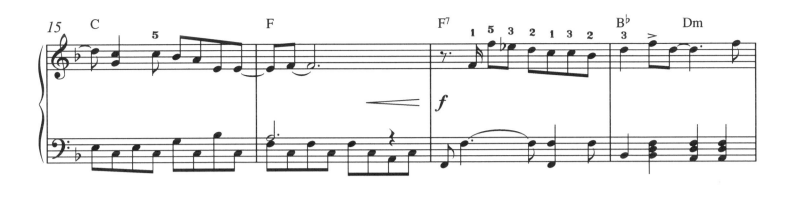

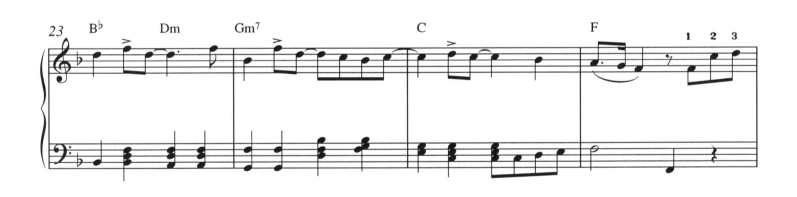
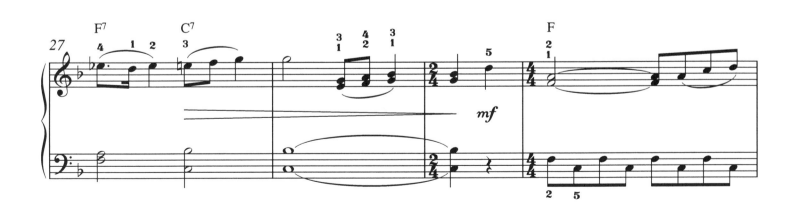

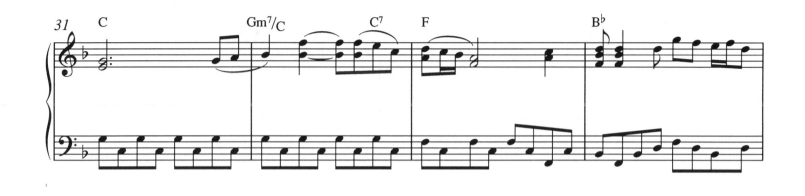

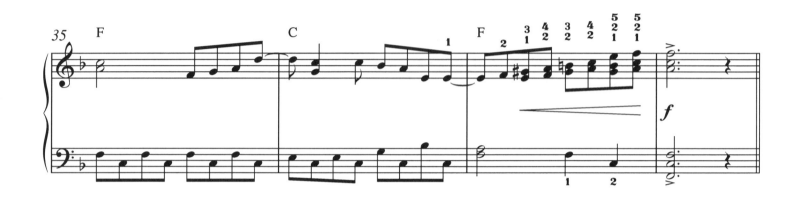

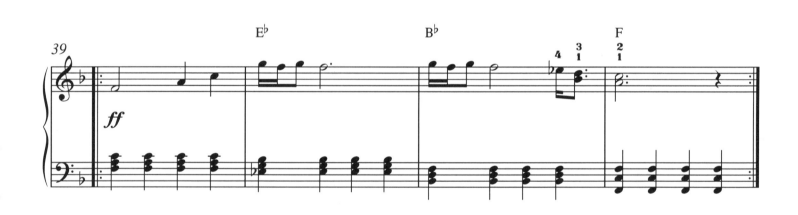

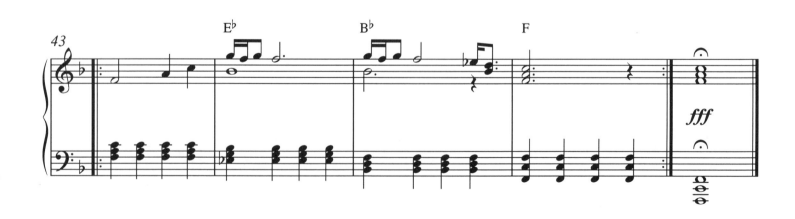

(EVERYTHING I DO)
I DO IT FOR YOU

Music by Michael Kamen

There is a strong feeling of eight quavers to the
bar in this arrangement. This is reflected in some
of the left hand passage work, but do not allow
the rhythm to become obtrusive.

WORDS

Words and music by Barry Gibb, Robin Gibb
and Maurice Gibb

This song needs to be played in a flowing style.
The left hand accompaniment figures should be
subservient, at all times, to the melody.

WITHOUT YOU

Words and music by Peter Ham and Tom Evans

This is essentially an expressive song, therefore the repeated notes in the melody, beginning at bar 3, need to be played with as delicate a touch as possible.

ITSY BITSY, TEENIE WEENIE, YELLOW POLKADOT BIKINI

Words and music by Lee Pockriss and Paul J. Vance

The humour of this song needs to be brought out, especially in the coda beginning at bar 29. You will need to practice the sixths in bar 35 slowly a few times in order to achieve fluency.

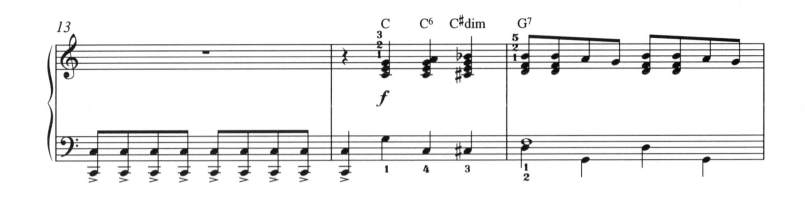

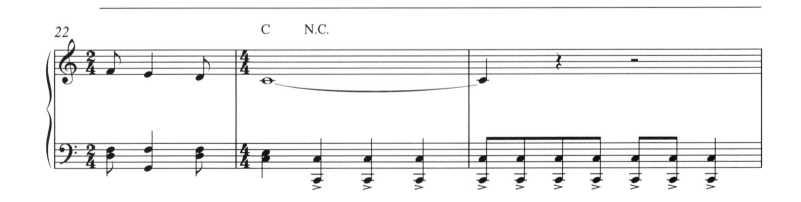

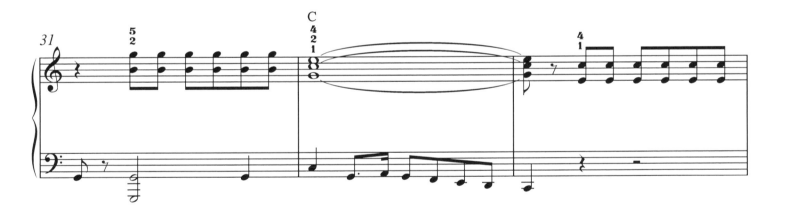

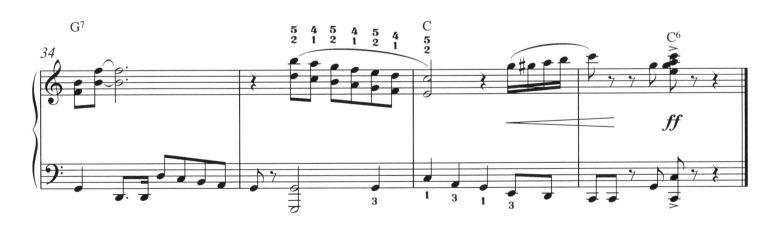

EVERY BREATH YOU TAKE

Words and music by Sting

This arrangement is characterised by considerable rhythmic drive. It will help you to keep the forward momentum if you think of the song in two bar phrases and put a slight accent on the first beat.

FERNANDO

Words and music by Benny Andersson, Stig Anderson
and Bjorn Ulvaeus

There is an effective contrast between the music
in the verse section and that of the chorus
beginning at bar 20. Try to convey this change by
bringing out the left hand figures.

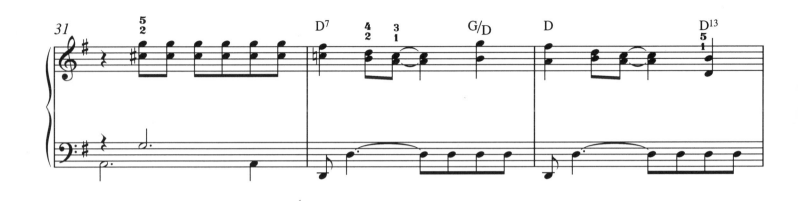

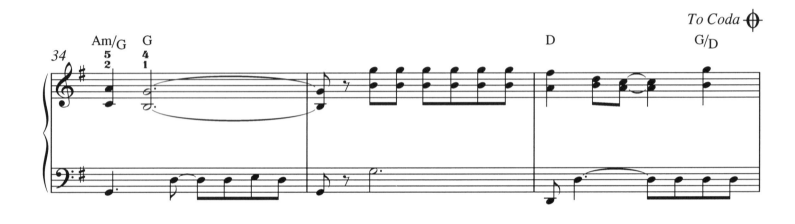

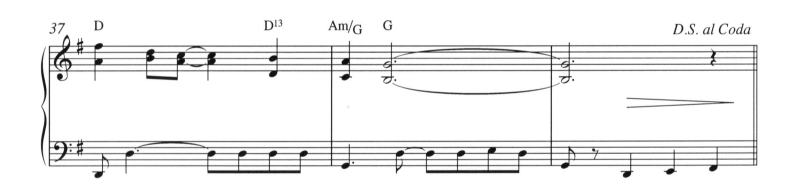

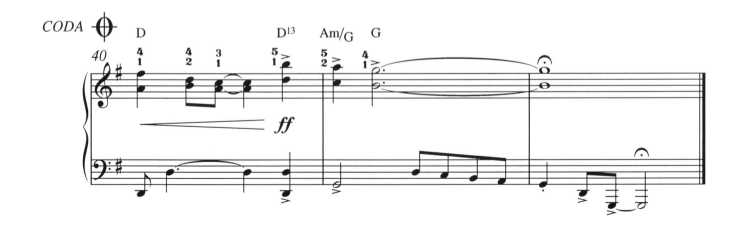